Grace Darling

Tim Vicary

Illustrated by Ashley Mims

Original Bookworms Series Editor:
Jennifer Bassett

Activities

Before reading

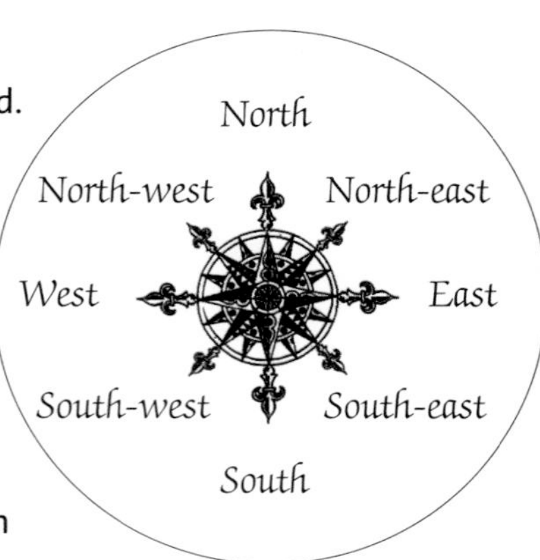

It was 1838, off the north-east coast of England. In a little wooden boat Grace Darling and her father were on an angry sea in the dark night, with huge waves all around them. The wind was screaming in their ears. They were trying to reach a rock. On the rock were cold, wet people, who were crying for help and fighting to stay alive. Their ship, the *Forfarshire,* was broken in two. Could Grace and her father save them? This is the true story of Grace Darling – a girl who became famous for being so brave on that stormy night.

1 Read the introduction to the story. Then tick the correct boxes.

		Yes	No
1	The story is true.	✓	
2	Grace Darling was a young man.		
3	The story happened in 1838.		
4	The *Forfarshire* was a ship.		
5	The story happened off the north-east coast of Scotland.		
6	It was a hot, dry night.		
7	Grace and her father were in a wooden boat.		
8	Some people were very cold on a rock.		
9	Grace Darling became famous.		

CHAPTER 1 The *Forfarshire*

The Times **London, 19th September 1838**

On the afternoon of 6th September the steamship *Forfarshire* started its journey from Hull to Dundee, in Scotland. There were sixty people on the *Forfarshire*, which was a comfortable, modern ship. There was a strong, north-east wind that afternoon, but at first no one was afraid . . .

Daniel Donovan was a passenger on the *Forfarshire*. He was a young man, about thirty years old. He stood on the deck of the ship and looked at the sea. It was difficult to stand on the deck, because the wind was so strong. The ship was moving up and down uncomfortably and Daniel felt ill. Then a big wave hit the side of the ship, and salt water flew into his face.

'The wind is getting stronger,' said a passenger beside him, called Mr Robb. 'And it's getting darker, too.' He was a tall, dark man with a black coat. He didn't like being at sea very much, and he looked worried.

'Yes,' said Daniel. 'I can't see the land now.' He looked to the west, but he could see no land and no lights. Only water – big grey waves with white tops, which went up and down, up and down.

'But the *Forfarshire* is a good modern ship,' said Mr Robb. 'Nothing can happen to a new ship like this. Listen to those fine strong engines!'

Daniel looked down at the big paddle wheel on the side of the ship. It went round and round, down under

deck the floor on a ship

wave (*n*) how the sea moves; a 'hill of water' in the sea

dark a colour that is not light, like black

land (*n*) the part of the world that is not the sea

engine a machine that makes a ship, car, etc. move

paddle wheel a large wheel on the side of a ship that moves through the water

smoke grey or black clouds from a fire

funnel a 'pipe' on top of a ship; smoke from the engine comes out of it

noise a loud sound

crash a loud noise when something hits something else

the white water and up again . . . under the water and up. Then he looked up at the black smoke that came from the *Forfarshire*'s funnel.

'Yes,' he said. 'They're good, strong engines.' But he was not really sure. He was an engineer, so he knew about engines. Sometimes the *Forfarshire*'s engines made strange noises, and the paddle wheels went round slowly. Then there was a crash, and they went quickly again. Daniel was not happy.

A sea bird flew low across the white tops of the big, grey waves. Daniel watched it and felt wind and rain on his face. Then a door opened behind him, and a woman screamed.

'Simon, come back! Come back at once!'

Daniel looked behind him and saw a small boy. He was running across the deck. He was only five years old, and the wind was much too strong for him. He fell over on the deck and started to cry. Then another big wave hit the side of the ship. The white water came onto the ship and carried the boy along the deck.

'Help!' the woman screamed. 'Save my child!'

Daniel put out his hand and caught the boy's coat. Then he carried him quickly back to his mother.

'Quick! Get back inside, out of the wind!' he shouted. He hurried through the door and closed it with a crash. 'It's too dangerous for children out there!'

fall over (*past* **fell over**) to go down suddenly

save to take someone out of danger

'Yes, I know,' the woman said. 'Come here, Simon!' She sat down and held the boy with one arm. She had another child next to her – a little girl, about seven years old. 'Thank you, sir,' she said.

The ship moved up and down very quickly, and Daniel sat down beside the woman. She smiled at him, but she looked very white and ill.

'I'm Daniel Donovan,' he said. 'What's your name?'

'Mary Dawson,' she said. 'This is my son Simon and my daughter Sarah.'

'Isn't your husband with you?'

'No,' she said. 'He's in Scotland. We're going home to see him. It's good we're in a strong, modern ship.'

'Yes,' said Daniel. Then for a few seconds he said nothing. It was quiet in this room. Much quieter than outside.

sir a polite word *for a man when* you speak to him

'Mr Donovan,' said Mrs Dawson suddenly. 'What's happened to the engines? I can't hear them now. Can you?'

Daniel listened. 'She's right!' he thought. 'The engines have stopped!' He could hear the noise of the wind and the sea, but not the engines. 'You're right, Mrs Dawson,' he said. He stood up and ran to the door. 'Excuse me. I . . .' But then he opened the door, and his words were lost in the wind.

Outside, he looked up at the ship's funnel. There was no smoke above it. He looked over the side of the ship at the big paddle wheels. He watched them for two minutes, but they did not move. And all the time the big grey waves lifted the *Forfarshire* up and down, and white water fell on the deck.

'What's happening?' shouted Mr Robb. 'Why aren't we moving?'

'The engines have broken down!' shouted Daniel. 'This isn't a sailing ship – it can't move without its engines!'

A big wave hit the side of the paddle wheel and sent white water over their heads. Some sailors were trying to put up a small sail, but the wind blew it out of their hands, away across the sea into the night.

'There are women and children on this ship,' shouted Mr Robb. 'It's nearly dark, and the weather is getting worse. What can we do?'

Daniel looked at him. 'I don't know, my friend,' he shouted back. 'I can't do anything! And I don't think anyone can help us now.'

word a thing that you say or write

lose (*past* **lost**) not to have something any more; not to know where to find something

break down (*past* **broken down**) to stop working

sailing ship a ship that uses wind to help it to move

nearly almost

Activities

1 Complete the sentences with these words.

waves | engines | deck | ~~steamship~~ | funnel | dark | paddle

1 The *Forfarshire* was a big, comfortable steamship .
2 Daniel Donovan stood on the ________________ of the *Forfarshire*, looking out to sea.
3 The sea was rough with big grey ________________ .
4 Mr Robb was a tall, ________________ man.
5 Black smoke came out of the *Forfarshire*'s ________________ .
6 There was a big ________________ wheel on each side of the ship that went round and round.
7 The ship's ________________ made strange noises, then stopped.

2 Put these sentences in the correct order.

a The engines made some strange noises. ☐
b The *Forfarshire* left Hull. [1]
c The engines stopped working. ☐
d Daniel Donovan saved Mrs Dawson's boy. ☐
e Some sailors tried to put up a small sail. ☐
f Daniel saw that there was no smoke above the funnel. ☐

3 Choose the correct answer.

1 The *Forfarshire* was travelling to . . .
a Hull in Scotland. ☐
b Dundee in Scotland. ☑
c Hull in England. ☐

2 It was windy, but people weren't scared, because . . .

a there were sixty people on the ship. ☐

b it was a north-east wind. ☐

c the ship was strong and modern. ☐

3 Daniel felt ill, because . . .

a the ship was moving up and down a lot. ☐

b a big wave hit the side of the ship. ☐

c it was nearly dark. ☐

4 Daniel knew about engines, because . . .

a he was an engineer. ☐

b he was a sailor. ☐

c he had travelled on a ship before. ☐

5 Mrs Dawson screamed, because . . .

a she was feeling ill. ☐

b her son fell over and water carried him along the deck. ☐

c she didn't like Daniel. ☐

6 The big paddle wheel stopped moving, because . . .

a there was too much smoke above the funnel. ☐

b the ship didn't have a big sail. ☐

c the engines had broken down. ☐

4 Find the words from the letters in brackets. Complete the sentences.

1 It was getting dark and Daniel couldn't see the ___land___. **(aldn)**

2 Mrs Dawson said, 'Thank you, ________,' to Daniel. **(ris)**

3 Grey waves ________ the *Forfarshire* up and down. **(filtde)**

4 The *Forfarshire* was a steamship, not a ________ ship. **(siailgn)**

5 Things you say or write are called ________. **(rdwos)**

mainland land that is not an island

lighthouse a tall building by the sea, with a strong light at night to tell ships about dangerous rocks

CHAPTER 2 The lighthouse

When the engines stopped, the *Forfarshire* was about five kilometres east of St Abbs Head, in Scotland. The ship was travelling north, from Hull to Dundee. But the wind came from the north, so the *Forfarshire*, without her engines, started to go south again, back to England. It was dark, and the wind was very strong.

About thirty kilometres south-east of St Abbs Head is a group of small rocky islands not far from the mainland. These are the Farne Islands. On one of them, Longstone Island, there is a lighthouse. There were three people in the lighthouse that night – William Darling, his wife Thomasin and their daughter Grace. Grace's brothers usually lived with them at the lighthouse, but that night they were in Bamburgh, on the mainland.

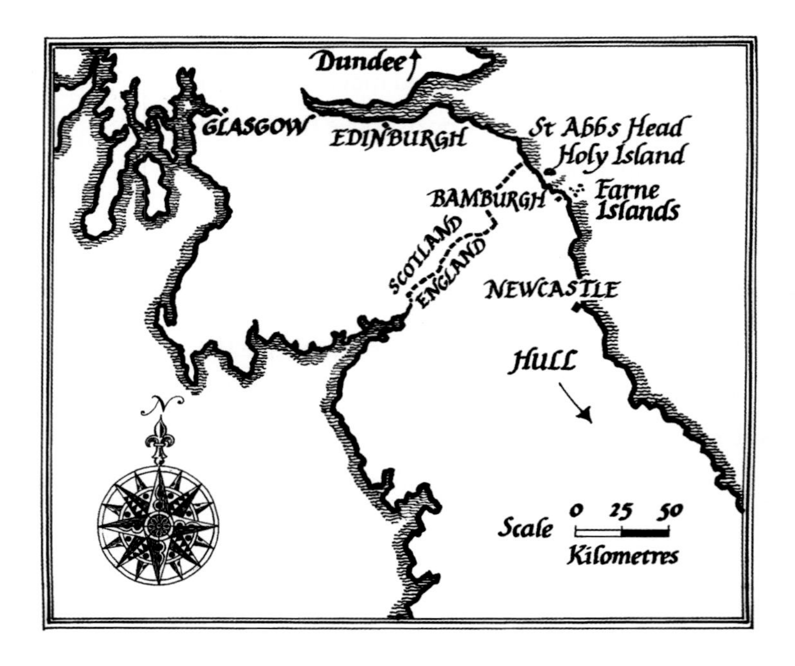

At seven o'clock William Darling went up the long stairs of the lighthouse to light the big oil lantern. Grace went with him. William Darling was a thin, strong man about fifty years old. He moved quickly and quietly. He had a candle in his hand. Sometimes he turned to talk to Grace, and the big brown eyes in his kind face shone in the candlelight.

Grace was a young woman about twenty-two years old. She was not very tall or strong. She had big brown eyes like her father and soft brown hair. She carried an oil can in one hand and held her long skirts with the other hand. She smiled at her father as they talked.

At the top of the lighthouse Grace and her father came into a small room. This room had no walls – just big windows all around. The noise of the wind and rain was terrible there, and they had to shout to hear each other.

Grace put oil in the big lantern in the middle of the room, and William lit it. When the lantern was burning, the big

light (*past* **lit**) to make a candle or lamp burn so that you can see in the dark

oil (*n*) a thick black liquid that you can burn

lantern a light in a glass box

candle a stick of wax that gives light when it burns

can (*n*) a metal box

silver mirrors started to move slowly around it. William Darling and his daughter stood and watched them. The rain crashed against the windows, and the wind screamed like an animal in the night.

'I hope the poor sailors will see this light,' shouted William. 'It's the blackest of nights out there. No moon, no stars – nothing but wind and rain and wild white water.'

'Let us also hope there are no ships near the rocks,' shouted Grace. 'The storm will wreck a ship that comes near them tonight.'

'That's true, lass,' said William. 'But we can do no more now. Let's go down to have our supper.'

The father and daughter went slowly down the dark stairs to the kitchen. Grace's mother, Thomasin, was putting the supper on the table. She was a white-haired woman of sixty-five.

'Did you see anything?' she asked.

'No, nothing,' William answered. 'Only the rain on the windows.'

'Thank goodness,' she said. 'You couldn't help anyone tonight, William. If there is a shipwreck, you won't be able to do anything. The boys aren't here to help you.'

'But, Mother,' Grace said. 'Father has to try to save people. It's his job. He can't leave them to die.'

'Grace, no man could row a boat by himself in this wild sea,' said Thomasin. 'So let us be glad that there are no poor ships near us, on this terrible night.'

'Yes, Grace, let us be glad for that,' said William. And so the three people sat quietly around their table in the warm kitchen. In the black night outside, the wind screamed, and the big waves crashed against the rocks, again and again and again.

mirror a piece of glass that you can see yourself in

wreck (*n*) a broken ship; (*v*) to break something completely

lass a girl

supper a meal you eat in the evening

row (*v*) to move a boat with oars

glad happy

warm quite hot, not cold

CHAPTER 3 In the engine room

'Mr Donovan!'

'Yes.'

'The captain wants to see you. You're an engineer, aren't you? Come this way, please.' The sailor opened a door, and Daniel went quickly inside. They went down some stairs. He opened another door, and a great cloud of steam came out. Daniel followed the young sailor into the room. It was very hot in there, and there were clouds of steam everywhere. A tall, red-faced man came up to him.

'Mr Donovan? My name's Humble, Captain Humble. We need you, sir. You're an engineer, I understand. One of these engines has already stopped, and the other one is working very badly. There's too much steam in this room, sir, and not . . .'

A big wave hit the ship with a terrible crash, and Daniel, Captain Humble and the young sailor held onto the wall. Daniel saw a big man in a blue coat and shouted to him.

'Are you the ship's engineer?'

'Yes!' The man looked angry, tired and frightened.

'What's the matter? Why has this engine stopped?'

'Why? Because it's too old, of course! Look here! See this? And this . . .' For five minutes the two engineers moved around in the steam and smoke and looked at the big engines.

'See? It's broken here and here! How can I mend it now, in the middle of a storm? Can you do that, sir?'

Daniel shook his head. He was angry and frightened. 'No, of course I can't! The ship must go back to land!'

The man agreed quickly. 'That's right, that's what I say! But you tell Captain Humble that! He says this is a new,

steam (*n*) hot wet air; water changes into steam at 100°C

follow to go after someone

hold onto (*past* **held onto**) to keep touching something

frightened afraid

broken not working

mend to make something work again

shake his head (*past* **shook his head**) to move his head from side to side, to say no

agree to say that you think the same as someone else

modern ship, so it can go anywhere, in any weather! Our rich passengers want to go to Scotland, so that's where we're going, he says! But it's too dangerous and . . .'

The man stopped when Captain Humble came near. 'Well, Mr Donovan? Can you help us? Do you know more about engines than this stupid engineer here? He says he can do nothing, and we must go back to Hull, because of a small storm! But I'm sure . . .'

'He's right, Captain Humble!' shouted Daniel. 'I can do nothing for these engines here, in this storm! They're too old, and this one is broken in three places! We must go back to land, Captain, or we will all drown! I cannot help you!'

'Gaaaaaargh!' The captain pushed Daniel angrily away from him. 'Then get out of my way, Mr Donovan – you're no good to me! Go back to the women and children!'

Daniel went quickly to the door and up the stairs to the wind and rain outside. But he was a badly frightened man. His hands were shaking, and it was hard for him to stand in the terrible screaming wind. Above his head two sailors were putting up a small sail. 'That's no good,' he thought. 'It's too small for a big ship like this. Without engines we can do nothing.'

He stared out to sea, but he could see nothing – only the white tops of the great black waves and the black clouds above. No stars, no moon. But – far away to the south-west – there was a little light flashing. On . . . off . . . on . . . off. It went behind a wave and then came back again, like a star in the night sky, far away.

But it was coming nearer. Nearer all the time.

near close

stupid not clever

drown to die in water because you cannot breathe

push to move quickly and strongly with your hands

get out of my way go away; I am angry with you

stare (*v*) to look hard at something for a long time

Activities

1 Correct the mistakes in these sentences.

1 The Farne Islands are small ~~flat~~ rocky islands.

2 There was a lightning on Longstone Island.

3 Grace Darling was William's son.

4 There was a big lampshade at the top of the lighthouse.

5 William and Grace went down to the kitchen to have lunch.

6 The man in charge of the *Forfarshire* was Lord Humble.

7 Daniel said they must go back to land or they would escape.

2 Find words in the word snake to complete the sentences.

mirrorscandlesteamstupidlitmainlandsave

1 Grace's brothers were in Bamburgh, on the mainland.

2 William Darling went up the stairs carrying a __________.

3 Grace put oil in the lantern, and William __________ it.

4 When the lantern was burning, big __________ moved around it.

5 Grace said that her father had to try to __________ anyone who was in trouble.

6 It was hot in the engine room, and there were clouds of __________.

7 Captain Humble said that the engineer was __________.

3 Match the two halves of the sentences.

1 The *Forfarshire* was travelling north, . . . [c]
2 Grace carried an oil can . . . [ ]
3 Thomasin said that William couldn't help anyone that night, . . . [ ]
4 The ship's engineer told Daniel that the engines were broken, . . . [ ]
5 The captain was angry and . . . [ ]
6 Daniel stared out to sea . . . [ ]

a and saw a little light flashing on and off.
b pushed Daniel away from him.
c but the strong wind blew the ship back south again.
d because no man could row a boat by himself in the wild sea.
e and Daniel agreed that no one could mend them.
f and put oil in the big lantern to make it burn.

4 Who said this? Write the names.

Captain Humble | Thomasin | ~~Grace~~ | Daniel | William

1 'The storm will wreck any ships that come near the rocks.' Grace
2 'That's true, lass. But we can do no more now.' ____________
3 'You couldn't help anyone tonight, William.' ____________
4 'We need you, sir. You're an engineer, I understand.' ____________
5 'The ship must go back to land.' ____________

5 What do you think happens next? Tick the boxes.

	Yes	No
1 William sees the ship.	[ ]	[ ]
2 The storm gets worse.	[ ]	[ ]
3 The *Forfarshire* crashes on some rocks.	[ ]	[ ]
4 Daniel manages to mend the engines.	[ ]	[ ]

CHAPTER 4 **Nothing to see**

It was half past two in the morning. In the lighthouse Grace was asleep in her room. It was a small, tidy room with white walls. Her dress was on the back of the door, and her other clothes were on a chair by the bed. There were some books on a desk and some sea-birds' eggs on a table.

Someone knocked at the door. 'Grace!' her father's voice called. 'Wake up, lass. I need you to help me.'

'What is it, Father?' She got up quickly and opened the door. William Darling stood there with a candle in his hand. He was wearing his big coat and heavy boots, and his hat was pulled down over his ears. His face was tired and wet with rain.

'The storm is worse. The wind is coming from the north now, and it's stronger. We have to go outside and tie the boat down, or we will lose it!'

'All right. I'll come down.' Quickly Grace closed the door and put her clothes on. She often got up in the night. There was always work on a lighthouse, and the sea did not wait for morning. A minute later she ran downstairs to the kitchen, put a coat over her thin dress, tied her hair under her hat and followed her father out into the night.

The wind nearly lifted her off her feet. It was strong and wet. She opened her mouth to call to her father, but the words blew away into the night. Her coat and dress blew out behind her like paper, and the rain hit her face, like small stones.

She walked slowly after her father, to the boathouse. Her father was carrying a small lantern, and in its light Grace saw a great wave of white water. It broke against

desk a table usually in a study or an office

tie (*v*) to put ropes round something to hold it still

thin not fat

the rock in front of the boathouse, and white water crashed against the boathouse doors. William shouted something to Grace, but she could not hear him – the noise of the wind and the sea was too loud, too terrible.

In the boathouse she helped her father to tie the boat down to the rock. They tied down the oars, too, so that nothing could move them. Then they ran outside and carried everything into the kitchen – their chickens, their fishing things. They couldn't leave anything outside on a night like this.

Before they went back in, Grace stared out into the night. The light from the top of the lighthouse flashed out over the water, and for thirty seconds she could see very well. One after another the big, black waves came out of the darkness – waves ten, twenty metres high! When they hit the rock, there was a huge crash, and white water flew everywhere, thirty, forty metres up over the Longstone rock.

oar a long piece of wood that you use to move a boat through water

Grace stared out, over the waves, past the rocks and islands. But – thank goodness! – she could see no lights, no ships. No ship could live in that sea tonight.

'Grace! Come on in, lass!' Her father held the door open behind her. She went in quickly, and he closed the door behind them. Her mother had warm drinks ready for them.

'Go to bed now, Father,' Grace said. 'You haven't slept yet tonight. Let me watch the light now, and Mother can come up at five.'

'All right, lass,' he said. William was very tired. He went upstairs with his wife, and in two minutes they were asleep.

Grace finished her drink quickly and changed out of her wet clothes. Then she went up alone to the room with the big windows at the top of the lighthouse. The wild wind screamed and shook the glass. It was half past three in the morning.

ready waiting

CHAPTER 5 The shipwreck

In the passengers' sitting room on the *Forfarshire* Mrs Dawson looked unhappily at Daniel, Mr Robb and two other men – Thomas Buchanan and James Kelly. Her two children were crying. 'I'm so frightened. Do you think we're going to die? What can we do, Mr Donovan, without the engines?'

'Not much, Mrs Dawson,' said Daniel slowly. 'But there are some islands south of here, called the Farne Islands. They are very near. I've seen the lighthouse flashing on them. I think the captain is trying to go into the quieter water between the islands and the mainland. I . . . I'm going to go outside again to see how near the lighthouse is. I'll come back and tell you.'

Daniel got up and went out into the night. It was raining hard now, and the wind was screaming from the back of the ship. He stared into the dark. He could see nothing in the west. Where was the light? He walked carefully across the ship to the other side. Suddenly he fell on the wet deck, and he caught the side of the ship with his hands. Then he looked up, and a light flashed into his eyes. There it was – the lighthouse, only three hundred metres away to the north!

'But this is wrong!' he thought. 'We're too close! Much too close! I must tell the captain!'

He stood up and started to run along the deck. But there in front of him a great mountain of white water flew into the sky . . . ten . . . twenty metres above the ship.

'Rocks!' screamed Daniel. 'Rocks! There are rocks in front of us, rocks all round! Captain! CAPTAIN!'

The captain was already shouting at the sailors, and

shipwreck a broken ship that can't travel any more

wrong not right

close when two people or things are near to each other

the ship was turning, turning to the west, away from the light. But it was too late. There was a great crash, and Daniel and all the sailors fell to the deck. Then another crash . . . and another. The waves lifted the *Forfarshire* and threw it onto the rock, like a child playing with a toy.

Daniel held onto a rope and stared into the dark. The light flashed again from the lighthouse. Then he looked back along the ship. People were running out onto the deck and screaming.

Then another very big wave hit the ship. White water flew everywhere and fell on Daniel like stones. He heard a terrible crash, and more water fell on him. He opened his eyes and looked back along the ship.

But there was nothing there.

Nothing but black water and more waves. The ship was broken in two, and the back of the ship, with the captain and all the rich passengers, was not there.

A voice shouted into the wind. 'Help us! Save us from the sea!' The door of the passengers' room was broken. But there were still some people inside the room – Mr Robb, Mrs Dawson and her two children, Mr Buchanan and James Kelly. Daniel went carefully back along the deck to the broken door. He put out his hand to touch it, and then a wall of white water hit the ship, and he could see nothing.

Activities

1 Complete the sentences and the crossword. Then find the mystery word to find out what Grace looks through in the next chapter.

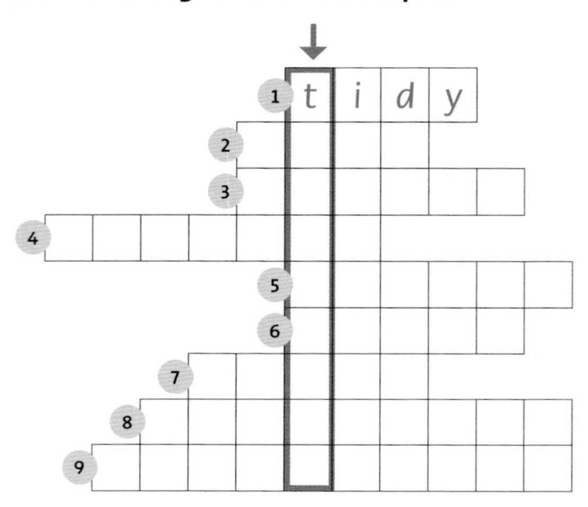

1 Grace's room was small and ___tidy___.

2 There were some books on Grace's ______.

3 There was ______ work on a lighthouse.

4 Grace and William ______ their chickens and fishing things into the kitchen.

5 Grace looked hard at the sea for a long time – she ______ at it.

6 Daniel saw that the *Forfarshire* was far too ______ to the lighthouse.

7 When something is not right, it is ______.

8 A broken ship is called a ______.

9 After the crash, the captain and many rich ______ were not there any more.

Mystery word: t______

2 Are these sentences true (T) or false (F)?

1 William Darling woke Grace up at three o'clock in the morning. [F]
2 William and Grace went to tie the boat down. [ ]
3 Grace went back to bed, and William watched the light. [ ]
4 Mrs Dawson told Daniel that she was feeling brave. [ ]
5 Daniel shouted that the rocks were too close to the ship. [ ]
6 There was a terrible crash, and the ship broke in two. [ ]

3 Correct the underlined words in these sentences.

1 William Darling was wearing his big black coat and heavy boats. boots
2 Grace's dress was thick. ______
3 Grace lied her hair under her hat. ______
4 In the boathouse Grace and William tied down the boat and the ears. ______
5 In the kitchen Thomasin had warm drinks steady for them. ______
6 Daniel held onto a rose. ______
7 A voice shouted, 'Help us! Wave us from the sea!' ______

4 What do you think happens next? Tick the boxes.

	Yes	No
1 Grace sees the wreck of the *Forfarshire*.	[ ]	[ ]
2 William notices some people in the sea.	[ ]	[ ]
3 Grace's brothers come back from the mainland.	[ ]	[ ]
4 Grace and her parents watch the wreck for two hours.	[ ]	[ ]
5 Grace says that if there are people alive, she can go out with her father.	[ ]	[ ]

Chapter 6 Out of the window

look after to do things for someone or something that needs help

At twenty to five that morning Grace felt a hand on her face. It was her mother. Grace was nearly asleep. The wind was screaming and shaking the big windows, and Thomasin Darling had to shout.

'Go to bed, Grace! It's nearly morning. I can look after the lantern now.'

'All right, Mother.' Grace got up slowly and went downstairs to her bedroom. It was much quieter in her room, because of the strong stone walls. She looked at the birds' eggs on her table, the books on the desk near the bed. The bed looked warm and comfortable. She smiled and started to get undressed.

A little grey light was coming in through the window. 'It's nearly morning,' she thought. 'I want to look at the sea before I go to sleep.'

She walked to the window and looked out. But she could see nothing, because of the salt and rain on the glass. 'It doesn't matter,' she thought. 'I'm too tired. I'm going to go to bed.'

But before she went to bed, she heard a mysterious voice in her head. '*Go to the window, Grace,*' it said. '*Go and look out.*'

So she got up, went to the window and opened it. The wind blew strongly into the room. It blew her hair across her face, and some books fell on the floor. In the grey morning light Grace looked out across the sea.

Most of the rocks and small islands were under water. Big white waves were breaking over them. The sea was wild, frightening, terrible. Grace looked, and felt cold. She could not remember a storm as bad as this. She thought of her warm bed and started to close the window.

Then she saw the ship.

It was a big ship on Harcar's Rock, about three hundred metres away to the south west. A very big ship, but it was broken in two, with white water breaking all over it. Grace could not see it very well, because of the rain and the sea.

'Father! Father! Come quickly!' She ran out of the room, down the stairs to her parents' bedroom. 'Come quick! There's a ship on Harcar's Rock! A big one – a passenger ship! It's broken in two!'

William Darling got out of bed in a second. He quickly got dressed and followed Grace up the stairs. 'Did you see any people?'

glass a window is made from glass; you can usually see through it

'No, Father. But it's difficult to see anything in this wild sea.'

Her father took a telescope from his pocket and stared out of Grace's window at the wreck of the *Forfarshire*. He looked for a long time, then said, 'I can see no one, but my eyes are old. You look, lass.'

Grace stared carefully through the telescope. White water crashed over the wreck. Sometimes the ship moved on the rock, and sometimes pieces of wood fell off into the sea. But she saw no people.

'No, Father. I think they have all drowned.'

'Poor, poor people.'

'Yes, but it's a good thing too, William.' Grace's mother was in the room now, and she was looking out of the window with her husband and daughter.

'Why is that, Thomasin?' William asked her.

'Why? Because the boys aren't here, William. You can't take a boat out in that wild sea alone. If there are people alive on that ship now, you won't be able to save them, William.'

'I could go with him, Mother,' said Grace quietly.

'Not in a sea like that, Grace,' her mother said.

Her father said nothing.

'We mustn't stop looking,' said Grace. 'There might be someone alive, and we can't just leave them to die.'

And so for the next two hours Grace and her parents watched the wreck of the *Forfarshire* through the telescope. Slowly daylight came. But they saw no people . . . only rain and waves and a broken ship in the wild angry sea.

telescope a long tube with special glass that makes things look bigger and nearer

pieces when something breaks, it changes from one thing into lots of these

daylight the light from the sun during the day

CHAPTER 7 On Harcar's Rock

There were twelve people on Harcar's Rock. Daniel Donovan was with Mrs Dawson and her children, and there were eight other people near them. The wreck of the *Forfarshire* was behind them, between them and the lighthouse.

They were nearly dead with wet and cold. Every two minutes white water fell on them. Daniel didn't have his coat any more, and the wind cut through his thin shirt like a knife. His hands and legs were red with blood. Mrs Dawson was crying and sat with her arms around her two small children. Mr Robb was shouting, begging someone to save them. Thomas Buchanan and the other men sat together, too cold to move. One man had a broken leg.

The waves got bigger, and the people on the rock moved closer together. After half an hour Mr Robb stopped shouting. Daniel looked at him. He was lying on the rock, his face white and cold. His eyes were open, but he did not see Daniel's hand in front of his face. He was dead.

'We'll all be dead soon,' shouted Thomas Buchanan angrily. 'No one can live long here, in this wind.'

'Why don't they come from the lighthouse to save us?' shouted James Kelly.

The lighthouse! Daniel remembered it suddenly. 'We must wave to it!' he shouted. 'They can't see us here! Come up onto the top of the rock! Wave to them!'

Daniel and James Kelly climbed to the top of the rock, but at first the others did not move – they were too cold, too tired, too frightened. Thomas Buchanan had to hit them and push them to the top of the rock.

The wind was very strong there, so it was difficult to

beg to ask someone *for* something you really need

lie to have all of your body on a bed or on the ground

wave (*v*) to move your hand through the air

stand. They held onto the rock and shouted and waved at the lighthouse as hard as they could.

No one answered. Behind the wild sea and the rain the lighthouse stood still and quiet. A few minutes later the light stopped flashing. But they saw nobody. One by one the men came down from the top of the rock and sat close together, out of the wind. Only Daniel and Thomas Buchanan stayed on top of the rock. They waved and shouted and cried, but they saw no one. Their faces were as cold as ice, and salty and wet from the sea.

stand (*past* **stood**) to be on your feet, not moving; not sitting

Activities

1 Are these sentences true (T) or false (F)? Correct the false sentences.

1 When Grace got ready for bed, it was nearly ~~night-time~~ morning. [F]

2 The *Forfarshire* was about three hundred metres away from the lighthouse. [ ]

3 Pieces of wood were falling off the ship. [ ]

4 At first Grace couldn't see the people, because a small boat was between Harcar's Rock and the lighthouse. [ ]

5 Thomas Buchanan died on Harcar's Rock. [ ]

6 After the men waved to the lighthouse, the light stopped flashing. [ ]

2 Who said this? Write the names.

James Kelly | Thomasin | ~~William~~ | Grace | Daniel | Thomas Buchanan

1 'I can see no one, but my eyes are old.' William

2 'If there are people alive on the ship, you won't be able to save them, William.' ______

3 'We mustn't stop looking.' ______

4 'No one can live long here, in this wind.' ______

5 'Why don't they come from the lighthouse to save us?' ______

6 'Come up onto the top of the rock! Wave to them!' ______

3 Rewrite these words from Chapters 6 and 7. Then complete each sentence with one word.

1 vawde w *aved* ____
2 rowddne d ____
3 eeltcspeo t ____
4 ssalg g ____
5 egbgnig b ____
6 tsnad s ____
7 borekn b ____

a There was salt and rain on the ____ of Grace's window.
b Grace and her father looked at the wreck through a ____ .
c Grace couldn't see any people and said they must have ____ .
d Mr Robb was shouting, ____ someone to save them.
e One man had a ____ leg.
f The wind was very strong, so it was difficult for the men to ____ .
g Daniel and Thomas *waved* and shouted and cried from the top of the rock.

4 What do you think happens next? Choose the best answer.

1 Grace Darling . . .
a sees people on Harcar's Rock. ☐
b stops looking through the telescope. ☐

2 The people on the rock . . .
a fall into the sea. ☐
b see that people in a boat have come to save them. ☐

3 Grace Darling talks angrily to . . .
a Thomasin. ☐
b William. ☐

CHAPTER 8 **The worst sea of the year**

Grace saw them first. Her mother was cooking breakfast in the kitchen, and her father was turning off the lantern. Grace was still looking out of her window through the telescope. For a second she saw a man on top of the rock, then she could not see him behind the waves. But a minute later she saw him again – and there were two men this time. They stood together and waved wildly. Then the rain came, and she could see nothing. But perhaps there were four, or five? She put down the telescope and called her father.

'Father, come quickly! There are men on the rock! They are still alive!'

William Darling ran into the room. He saw them. He put down the telescope and looked at his daughter.

'We must go, lass,' he said quietly. 'You and I. We must take the boat and save them. Will you come?'

'Of course, Father,' she said. 'If we don't save them, who will?'

'That's right, lass.' William Darling looked out of the window unhappily. 'I've not seen a worse sea this year. No boat could come from the mainland in this wind.'

Grace's mother came into the room and heard him. 'You can't go, William!' she said. 'Grace is only a girl. Look at that sea! You'll both drown!'

'We have to try, Mother!' said Grace angrily. 'Think of those poor people, alone on that rock. We live on a lighthouse – it's our job!'

'It's a job for your father and brothers, Grace, not you! You'll drown! How will that help those men?'

'How will it help them if we do nothing?'

Thomasin Darling looked out of the window again at the wild, angry sea. She shook her head. 'Perhaps you'll get to the rock, Grace,' she said. 'With good luck and the wind behind you. But you won't get back here against the wind. Not one man and a girl in a storm like this.'

William Darling took his wife's hands in his. 'Listen to me, Thomasin,' he said. 'There are three or four seamen on that rock. Strong men. They'll help us row back, if we save them.'

'*If* you save them,' said Thomasin. 'And if you don't . . . ?'

At first William Darling did not answer. He looked into his wife's eyes. 'We're going, Thomasin,' he said quietly. 'We have to go. Come down now and help us with the boat.'

Outside in the terrible wind and the rain it took them fifteen minutes to get the boat ready. Three times the waves nearly broke the boat on the rock. William got into the boat first and sat at the front. Grace and her mother held the boat away from the rocks. William got two oars ready and waited for the next wave.

'All right, Grace! Get in *now*!' he shouted.

Grace jumped into the boat, and William pulled hard with the oars. One . . . two . . . three pulls, and then a wave lifted the boat, and the oars were pulling at air. But they were away from the rocks. The boat came down between two waves, and Grace quickly took her oars. They both pulled hard together, but carefully, too. They did not want to lose an oar in the wild water. Grace was cold, and her dress and hat were wet. She was afraid, but happy and excited too. 'I'm glad we're going,' she thought. 'We must try to save those poor people.' At the top of a wave she could easily see across the Longstone rock to the other side. Then the boat went down between the waves, and

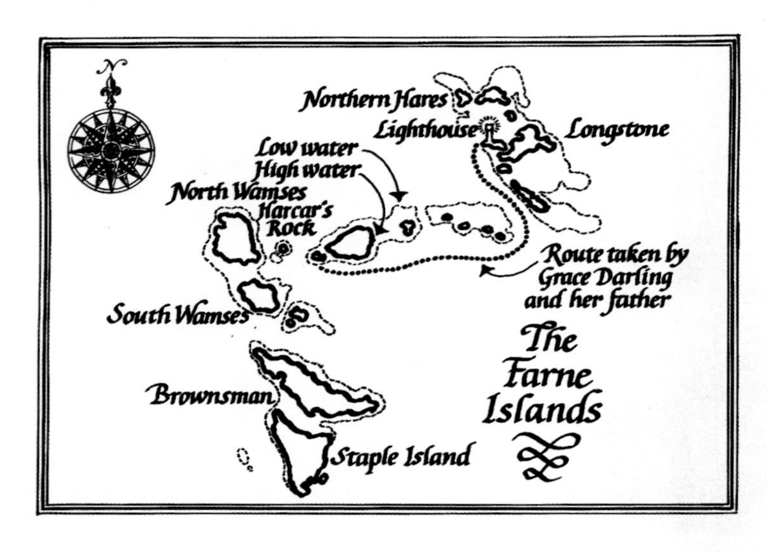

anxiously worriedly and excitedly

she could see only mountains of wild water everywhere.

'Pull left! Left!' William shouted. 'We must keep the rocks between us and the worst waves!'

Grace pulled hard at her oars and watched the waves. 'I hope we can save them!' she thought anxiously.

Outside the lighthouse Thomasin Darling watched the little boat. She saw it for a second, then it went behind a wave and came up again. 'It's not possible,' she thought. 'No boat can make a journey in a sea like that! Oh, I hope I won't lose my husband and daughter!'

She watched, and the little boat got smaller and smaller on the wild, grey sea.

CHAPTER 9 A little boat

'Help me, Mr Donovan! Please help!'

'How can I help you?' Daniel shouted to Mrs Dawson. 'How can anyone help?' He was too cold, too frightened, too tired. He couldn't think now.

'Please help my children!' cried Mrs Dawson. 'Keep them warm for me – they're so cold!'

It was true. The children were cold – very cold. Their eyes were open, but they were not moving. He tried to warm them with his hands. He shook them, but they did not move.

'It's no good!' he said. 'No one can . . .'

'They're not dead yet!' screamed Mrs Dawson. 'I know they're not dead!' She looked into her children's faces. 'Wake up, Simon! Sarah! Someone will save us soon. Please don't die!'

Daniel was tired and angry. 'Don't be stupid!' he shouted at her. 'We're all going to die, don't you understand? No one knows we're here!' He turned and stared at the wild, empty sea.

Mrs Dawson stared at him. Her face was wet with rain, and her hair was blowing in her eyes. 'Someone *must* come!' she shouted. 'We can't die here! Go to the top of the rock and look again! Tell them about my children!'

'Your children are . . .' But he was afraid to say it. He turned away, feeling very angry, and climbed to the top of the rock. The wind screamed in his ears. He looked across to the lighthouse and saw nothing – only waves and more waves. 'I hate the sea!' he thought. 'It's like a great grey animal with a hundred white teeth. I hate it! It wants to kill us all!'

keep (*v*) to help someone carry on doing something or being something

empty with nothing inside

hate the opposite of 'to love'

kill to end someone else's life

And then he saw the boat.

He saw it only for a second. It was on top of a white wave. It went down behind the wave, but then it came up again. Down and up again. And it was coming nearer! A little boat with two people in it. He held the rock and stared at it. The boat came nearer, and nearer again. Then a great wave like a mountain came, with white angry teeth, and the little boat went down behind it.

'No!' Daniel cried.

The boat came up on top of the wave, with white water

all around it. The oars were up, out of the water. For a second the boat started to turn on its side, then the oars went down into the water, and the boat came down the side of the wave. Daniel could see the two people in the boat now. One was a man. One was a young woman.

He got up and ran down the rock. He was crying and laughing at the same time. 'It's all right, Mrs Dawson!' he shouted.

'It's all right! Look there! Look! Someone *has* come to save us!'

Activities

1 Choose the correct answer.

1 Who first sees the people on the rock?
  a William ☐
  b Grace ☑
  c Thomasin ☐
2 Why is Grace angry?
  a Grace wants to save the people, but Thomasin says it's too dangerous. ☐
  b Grace wants her brothers to go in the boat with William. ☐
  c Grace doesn't want to go in the boat. ☐
3 How many oars are there in the boat?
  a six ☐
  b four ☐
  c two ☐
4 Why is Grace excited and happy?
  a She likes wild water. ☐
  b It is the first time that she has been in a boat. ☐
  c She wants to save the people even if it is dangerous. ☐
5 What is the matter with Mrs Dawson's children?
  a They are dead. ☐
  b They are ill. ☐
  c They are frightened. ☐
6 Who still believes that someone will save them?
  a Mrs Dawson's daughter Sarah ☐
  b Daniel ☐
  c Mrs Dawson ☐
7 Who first sees the boat?
  a Mrs Dawson ☐
  b Daniel ☐
  c Thomas Buchanan ☐

2 Put these sentences in the correct order.

a It takes them a long time to get the boat ready. ☐

b Grace sees men waving on Harcar's Rock. 1

c William gets in the front of the boat, then Grace jumps in. ☐

d William decides that he and Grace will try to save the people. ☐

e Daniel shouts at Mrs Dawson and says that they will all die. ☐

f Daniel sees the boat. ☐

g Thomasin watches as the little boat gets smaller and smaller. ☐

3 Complete the sentences with these words.

keep ~~alive~~ lose row hates anxiously

1 Grace says that there are men on the rock who are still *alive* .

2 'I hope we can save them,' thinks Grace ______________ .

3 William says that strong men will help to ______________ the boat back.

4 Thomasin doesn't want to ______________ her husband and daughter.

5 Mrs Dawson asks Daniel to ______________ her children warm.

6 Daniel doesn't like the sea – he ______________ it.

4 What do you think happens next? Tick the boxes.

	Yes	No
1 Some people are left on the rock.	☐	☐
2 Someone falls into the sea.	☐	☐
3 Grace rows the boat by herself.	☐	☐
4 The storm dies down.	☐	☐

CHAPTER 10 **Too many people**

Grace looked quickly behind her and saw the people on the rock. They were waving, shouting, laughing. But there were eight, nine, perhaps ten of them! Too many for this small boat.

She looked back at the waves and pulled hard and carefully with her oars. It was more than a kilometre around the islands from the lighthouse to the ship, and every wave, every rock was different and dangerous. She was tired now, but the job was not finished. The wrecked ship on Harcar's Rock was still fifty metres away.

'How many can you see, Grace?' her father shouted.

She looked again. 'Ten . . . twelve perhaps,' she said. 'It's too many, Father. We'll all drown, if they try to get in.'

'Yes. Put me on the rock, lass, and then take the boat out again,' shouted William. 'I'll talk to them. We can't take more than five, the first time.'

It was very dangerous near the rock. In the best place the waves went up and down two or three metres every minute. 'If we make one mistake,' Grace thought, 'the boat will break into fifty small pieces, and we'll be on the rock with the others.'

Carefully, slowly Grace and her father tried to get the boat near the rock, but three times they had to pull away at the last minute. Then, the fourth time, William Darling jumped. The passengers pulled him onto the rock.

Grace quickly rowed the boat out to sea again. She was alone in the boat now, and the boat moved differently. She was tired, and her arms and back were hurting. But she knew about boats. 'Watch the sea all the time,' she thought. 'The waves must meet the front of the boat first,

mistake something you do wrong

at the last minute just before doing something

or the boat will turn over. Forget the cold and the rain and the wet.'

On the rock William Darling spoke quickly. 'I'm going to take the woman back with me,' he said. 'And that man there, with the broken leg. Then I need three strong men to help me row the boat.' He looked at Daniel Donovan and two others. 'You, man, and you and you. The others must wait here. We'll come back for you later.'

'No! Why me?' shouted James Kelly. 'I want to come now!'

'You're going to stay here, sir!' shouted William angrily. 'Don't you understand? If you get in the boat, we'll all drown!'

'And my children,' cried Mrs Dawson, 'don't forget my children!'

William looked at her unhappily. He held out his arms. 'Give the children to me,' he said.

Carefully he took the boy and the girl from her and put the little bodies on the rock, near the sea. They were dead and cold. 'We can do nothing for them,' he said. Then he spoke quickly and quietly to Daniel Donovan. 'When the boat comes, help me get the woman in. We can't take her children.'

Daniel agreed. William put his arm around Mrs Dawson and waved to Grace.

Carefully, slowly she rowed the boat in to the rock. It was harder without her father. The wind and the waves moved the boat more quickly, and Grace was very tired now. One mistake meant death for them all. She came closer – twenty metres, ten, seven, five . . . A big wave lifted the boat, then a smaller one behind it. She pulled hard on the oars and threw a rope to a man on the rock. Then her father got into the boat, with the woman in his arms. She was screaming.

'My children! Bring the children, please!'

'No, we can't.' William Darling took the oars. 'Help her, Grace.'

Grace went to the back of the boat with the woman and held her. Daniel Donovan and two other men got in. They were carrying the man with the broken leg. The front of

mean (*past* **meant**) to be the reason for something

the boat was very near the rock now – too near. Grace looked behind her and saw a big wave.

'Pull, Father!' she shouted. 'Pull hard!' She stood up and pushed against the rock with an oar. The boat was very heavy now, with all these people in it.

William pulled hard with his oars. The big wave came in and broke into white water all around them. But the boat did not hit the rock. William pulled again and shouted. 'You men, help me! Take the oars!'

The little boat was very full. The sides were only just above the water, and often the water came in. Grace threw the water out with her hat. The wind and waves were against them now, and the four men had to row hard. But slowly, very slowly the lighthouse came nearer. At last, from the top of the waves, they could see Thomasin Darling. She was standing in front of the lighthouse and waving to them.

They were very tired when they got to the lighthouse. William and Daniel carried the man with the broken leg into the kitchen, and Grace and her mother helped Mrs Dawson.

Inside the kitchen William smiled at his daughter. 'You did a good job, lass,' he said. 'Thank you.'

'Let me come back again with you, Father,' she said.

'No,' he said. 'You're too tired. I can take two of these men.' He looked at Daniel and the other two men. 'Which are the strongest?' he asked.

Daniel was very tired. There was a fire in the kitchen – a warm, beautiful fire. He wanted to lie down in front of the fire and go to sleep for a long, long time. But William Darling's quiet brown eyes were looking at him.

'I'll come with you,' Daniel said.

'I'll come too,' said Thomas Buchanan.

William Darling smiled. 'Good men,' he said. 'Can you two men row as well as my daughter?'

Daniel looked at Grace, who was busy helping Mrs Dawson. She looked very small here in the kitchen – like any young woman. 'I'll try,' he said.

'Right,' said William. 'Come on then.'

So Daniel and Thomas Buchanan followed the old lighthouseman away from the warm kitchen fire, out into

full with lots of things or people inside

lie down to put all of your body on a bed or on the ground

busy to have lots of things to do

the rain and wind again. Daniel looked at the angry sea with its terrible waves, and he felt cold and frightened.

He remembered the small young woman alone in the boat by Harcar's Rock. 'That girl was strong and brave,' he thought. 'I need to be strong and brave, too, like her.'

Daniel was wet and very, very tired. But he got back into the boat with the other two men, and rowed out again into the wild, stormy sea.

The Times **London, 19th September 1838**

Mr Darling and his young daughter saved nine people from the wreck of the *Forfarshire*. The storm lasted for three days, and they stayed all that time with the Darlings in the lighthouse.

Queen Victoria thinks that Grace Darling is one of the finest young women in this country, and she is writing to thank her. One hundred years from now people will remember this day.

1 Choose the correct word to complete these sentences.

1 When Grace and William arrived at the rock, Grace was *tired* / *angry*.

2 Grace knew that waves must meet the *front* / *back* of the boat first.

3 William decided that *all* / *some* of the people should go in the boat.

4 On the way back to the lighthouse *four* / *two* men rowed the boat.

5 The little boat was *full* / *empty* and the sides were only just above the water.

6 Grace threw water out of the boat with her *hat* / *hands*.

7 In the lighthouse Grace helped *Mrs Dawson* / *Daniel*.

2 Put the letters in the correct order to make words to match the definitions.

1 Broken at sea by a storm or by crashing onto rocks. (**crwekde**) wrecked

2 Something you do wrong. (**simatek**) ________

3 With lots of things or people inside. (**lluf**) ________

4 To put all of your body on a bed or on the ground. (**eli wodn**) ________

5 When you have lots of things to do. (**ybsu**) ________

3 Sometimes people think differently about something that has happened. What do you think about this story? Tick the boxes.

1 The captain of the *Forfarshire* was doing his job well. He wanted to take his ship and passengers to Scotland, and he was right not to go back to land. ☐

2 Thomasin Darling didn't want Grace and William to go to the rock. She was right, because it was a very stupid and dangerous thing to do. ☐

3 Grace Darling became famous only because she was a young woman. William Darling, Daniel Donovan and Thomas Buchanan were also very brave, like Grace. ☐

4 *Grace Darling* is not a special story. Grace and William Darling were only doing their jobs. People like firemen and policemen save people every day. ☐

Activities

4 Thomasin Darling wrote a letter to her son William, telling him about the stormy night. Correct the underlined words.

Longstone
The Lighthouse, ~~Staple~~ Island

Dear William,

I have so much to tell you! We have had a terrible storm here. It lasted for forty-eight hours, and the waves were more than two metres high! A ship called the *Scotland* was wrecked on the beach. It was a small ship and it broke into four pieces. Some of the passengers climbed onto Harcar's Rock. I was the first person to see the shipwreck and the passengers waving on the rock. Your father and Grace then got the boat out and rowed to the rock, but only four people could get in our little boat. The passengers did not help to row the boat back, and then your father and one other man went to the rock a second time and saved four more passengers.

Your sister Grace is now famous, and the King is writing to thank her – it's in all the newspapers!

Come home soon.

From Mother

5 Complete the crossword with words from the story.

ACROSS

1 Grace watched the ship through this.

5 The name of the ship.

7 You row a boat with two of these.

9 Land which is not an island.

12 Completely broken.

DOWN

2 The Darling family lived in this.

3 Grace put this in the big lantern.

4 The ship was going in this direction, from Hull to Dundee.

6 A man who works on a ship.

8 Longstone Island was one of these islands.

10 The floor on a ship.

11 To move a boat with oars.

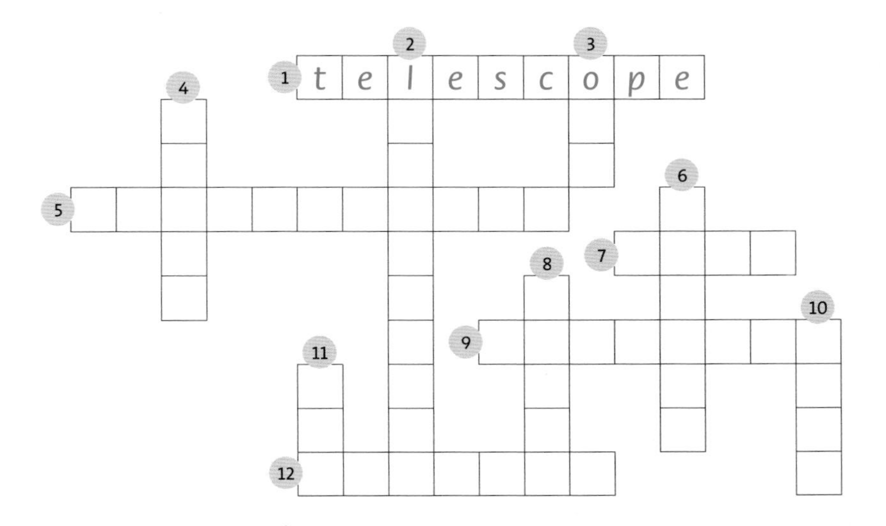

Project

1 Circle the things that can mean danger for a ship.

strong wind	fish	islands
blue skies	snow	very deep water
rocks	big waves	other big ships
sea birds	very hot sun	small sailing boats
heavy rain	storms	the dark

Here are some reasons. You can add your own reason.

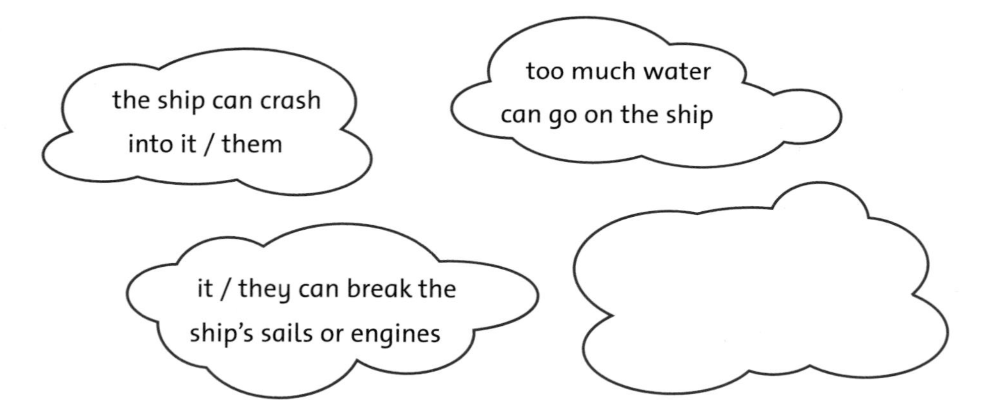

Now write sentences.

Rocks can be dangerous for a ship, because the ship can crash into them.

__________ can be dangerous for a ship, because __________

__________ can be dangerous for a ship, because __________

__________ can be dangerous for a ship, because __________

2 Imagine you're in a small boat at sea. Choose words from each cloud to complete the sentences.

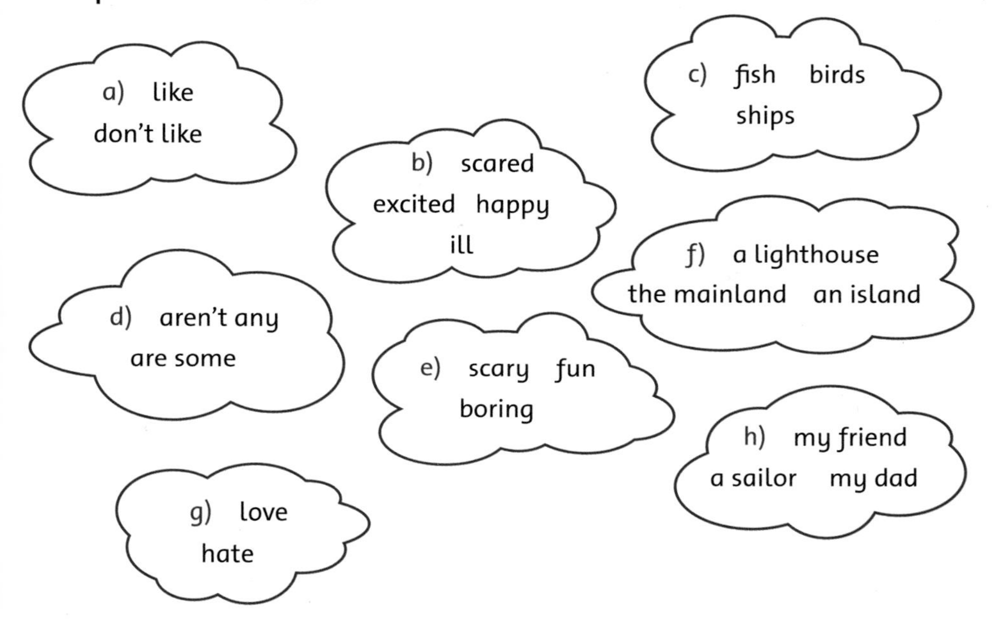

1 I a) ________________ being in a small boat at sea. It makes me feel b) ________________ .

2 From my boat I can see c) ________________ .

3 I hope that there d) ________________ big waves in the sea. When you're in a small boat, big waves are e) ________________ .

4 When I look through my telescope, I can see f) ________________ .

5 I g) ________________ being on my own in this boat.

6 Next time I go in a small boat, I want h) ________________ to come with me.

OXFORD
UNIVERSITY PRESS
Great Clarendon Street, Oxford OX2 6DP
Oxford University Press is a department of the University of Oxford.
It furthers the University's objective of excellence in research, scholarship, and education by publishing worldwide in
Oxford New York
Auckland Cape Town Dar es Salaam Hong Kong Karachi
Kuala Lumpur Madrid Melbourne Mexico City Nairobi
New Delhi Shanghai Taipei Toronto
With offices in
Argentina Austria Brazil Chile Czech Republic France Greece
Guatemala Hungary Italy Japan Poland Portugal Singapore
South Korea Switzerland Thailand Turkey Ukraine Vietnam
OXFORD and OXFORD ENGLISH are registered trade marks of
Oxford University Press in the UK and in certain other countries

First published 2010
2016
10 9 8

ISBN: 978 0 19 480286 4
Printed in China
This book is printed on paper from certified and well-managed sources.
ACKNOWLEDGEMENTS
Illustrations by: Ashley Mims/Melissa Turk & The Artist Network
Maps by: Brian Walker